W9-BFA-089

THE MOON of the WILD PIGS

THE MOON
of the
WILD PIGS

BY JEAN CRAIGHEAD GEORGE

Illustrated by Peter Parnall

Thomas Y. Crowell Company   New York

By the Author

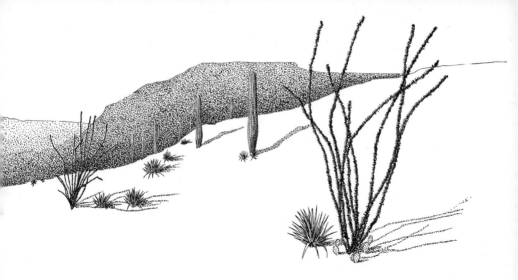

In the blasting heat of the desert a small wild piglet stood alone. He was crying. His whimpers did not carry far, for the desert is big and its heat seems to burn up even the loudest sounds.

The sky above held only the sun. The moon had disappeared hours ago. Not a cloud passed to cut the solar fire, for the moon of July was upon the land, the hottest season in the Northern Hemisphere. It is also the season of more lightning and thunder than any other.

Nowhere in the United States is July hotter or its storms more crashing than on the North American Desert, a vast dry land that lies within the western United States and northern Mexico. Each year only a shadow of rain falls on this bowl of clay and volcanic ash. In New England a generous sixty inches wet down the hills. In the Pacific Northwest, a drenching one hundred and forty-five create the noble rain forests. A desert, however, is a land where only one to twelve inches of rain fall a year, sometimes all at once.

Thirteen deserts lie around the world. Some, like sections of the Sahara in North Africa, have little life. Others are green with trees and cacti. They teem with birds and beasts. One of these is the Sonoran, part of the North, or Great, American Desert and the piglet's home. Around Tucson, Arizona, two rainy seasons come to this desert. Drizzles in winter and thunderous storms in summer moisten the land. All the other months the sun burns in bright skies.

In the Sonoran Desert, on one side of the Tucson Mountains, the piglet lived with his clan. He dwelt among cacti and mesquite, poisonous rattlesnakes, Gila monsters, and scorpions. He was a peccary piglet, a little animal unique to the New World. He was neither a wild boar nor a domestic pig, but he was piglike.

Certain differences set the peccaries apart from the true pigs. Pigs have many young at one time, the peccary but two. Peccaries have musk glands

on their rumps, dewclaws high on the inside of each hind foot, and two other toes on the hind feet. Pigs have neither scent glands nor dewclaws, and they have four toes on each hind foot.

A yard long and a little less than two feet high, adult peccaries weigh at the most fifty pounds as compared to a hundred and fifty for pigs. Unlike domestic pigs, their tails are barely visible. A collar of pale bristles around their necks give those of the Sonoran Desert the name collared peccary. One of two species in the Americas, they range from the southwestern United States to Patagonia. Although some collared peccaries live in the brushlands of Texas, in Arizona the deserts are their favorite homes. Heat, spiny plants, and deadly creatures are as normal to the peccaries as a meadow to a meadowlark.

The piglet was but two months old. He could have been born any day of the year, for peccaries have no special season to give birth to their young. He happened to have been born in May and consequently he did not know about July in the desert. He had run across the burning rocks beneath the white hot sun when he should have been asleep.

The saw-toothed tops of the purple mountains

loomed around him. Below their peaks giant
saguaro cacti speared the sky like green telephone
poles and in the sweeping distance a yellow valley lay dusty in the sun.

It was almost noon, the time of day when peccaries sleep. So hot is the desert at this hour that
even the green of the mesquite trees looks faded
in the brilliant light.

The piglet hurried on despite the heat. He cried
once more, then peered behind a cactus, hunting
for his mother and his clan of peccaries. He was
hopelessly lost.

Only a few hours ago he had been walking with the clan. Nine members, old, young, and intermediate, made up this average-sized group. Larger groups have as many as fifty members. His own clan had been moving up the side of the Tucson Mountains, and this confused the piglet. Climbing in the heat of the day was not part of their routine. Rather, they retreated to caves on the bank of the Santa Cruz Wash, a waterless river. In the cooler hours, at twilight and predawn, they wandered great distances looking for food. Like all peccaries, they ate prickly pear cacti by the sticky mouthful as well as fruits, berries, and roots. Occasionally they would find a waterhole and drink. Although they tended to stay around the Tucson Mountains they would sometimes go down to the valley and not come back for weeks.

This morning the gray boar, who often led the clan because he was the oldest and most experienced member, had sniffed the winds for many minutes. He had rattled his tusks, canine teeth that are digging tools and weapons on the peccary. The other adult boars, five in number, had rattled their tusks, too. The piglet's mother clattered her teeth.

Her worried sound had sent the piglet scampering under her four short legs, a safe position from which he watched the desert. He could see nothing to fear. No enemies were in sight: not the mountain lion or the coyote or the bobcat. The mourning doves called softly. All seemed well to the piglet, but apparently not to the boar.

He grunted as he lifted his long tapered face toward the south. Here the thunderstorms of July formed as hot winds blew over the Gulf of Mexico and lifted the water into clouds. Finally the boar rubbed his musk gland against another boar to exchange good odors. Other peccaries rubbed musk. When every member's scent was mixed, the clan smelled different from any other clan. This odor enabled them to find each other if they became separated.

The boar, satisfied that his clan smelled perfectly right, grunted once more, then led them out of the cave, across the volcanic rocks, and up the middle of the wash. They all followed quickly

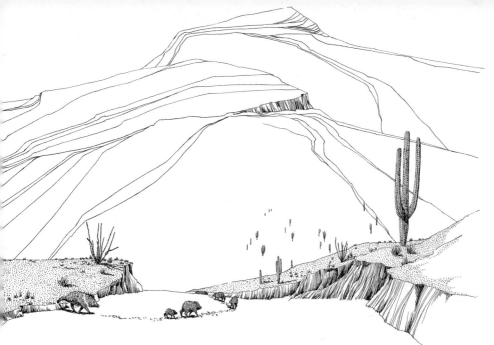

and quietly except the piglet. He whined and turned back. His mother nosed him forward. Obeying reluctantly, he tapped along behind until he came to the Red Rock, a mountain of a boulder that jutted out of the land. Here the wash changed its course as it cut around the rock, then spread out like a fan across the desert.

As they trotted around the Red Rock the piglet saw a spiny lizard dart out of a clump of brown brittle grass. It ran up the wash. Absentmindedly, the piglet clattered after it, his cloven hoofs clinking on the hot stones. He scurried across the waterless river. Its ripples and eddies were hot sand, its waterfalls were cracked clay. The lizard sped under a greenish stone. The piglet ran right past him, realized he was alone and, turning around, squinted toward the Red Rock. Every member of his clan had disappeared.

This did not frighten him, for he was very confident. So devoted and gentle were the members of his clan to him and to each other that the piglet knew only contentment.

This feeling had begun about an hour after his birth in the green light under the paloverde tree. He had been born in the tall grasses together with a sister. His mother waited for him to stand up, which took about two hours, then she led him and his sister down the peccary-scented trail to meet the clan. This moment had been warm and reassuring. The boar had greeted him first. He had sniffed the rabbit-sized tan piglet for many minutes. Then, nudging him gently with his long nose, he turned to sniff the piglet's sister.

One by one all the other peccaries walked over to him, scented, and also accepted him. Two females had been so pleased with him they had tried to take him. His mother shouldered them off.

When the meeting was done the piglet followed his mother and sister to the shade of a cactus. They

all lay down. He nursed, was snuggled, and had never known a fear from that day to this. He lived in a clan that surrounded and protected him.

As he grew older his own personality led him into problems. Once he had watched his mother carefully avoid a cholla cactus. This, the jumping cactus, has twiglike joints bristling with spines that break off at the lightest touch. Once broken, these balls of needles fairly leap onto the passerby. The piglet, curious, approached the cactus his mother

had circumvented. A joint pierced his skin and sent him squealing to his clan. A swift strike of his mother's hoof dislodged the painful spikes.

Other cacti, he learned, were peccary food. Every day the clan would chew and swallow, spines and all, the round discs of the prickly pear cactus. This plant was not nourishing to most animals, but the peccaries gained weight on it. It was, more important, full of water, and the pigs quenched their thirst with each splintery bite.

On this day in July, the lost piglet put his nose to the ground and searched for his own trail. He instinctively knew to trace it home. But it was nowhere. He stood still. The temperature was rising. Eighty degrees at dawn, the desert air was now a hundred and two. The sunlight was like a hot iron on his back. The piglet plunked heavily to the left and lay down under a paloverde tree.

A true desert tree, this spreading plant adjusts to waterlessness by dropping its leaves. This keeps the water from transpiring through them and drying the tree up. The yellow-green trunks and limbs make life-giving chlorophyll when the leaves are gone.

Beside the paloverde grew another plant that had no leaves during the long drought, the ocotillo (oh ko tee' yo). Gray and withered, its limbs looked like pencils standing in a cup. The ocotillo simply waited, dormant, for the rains.

The piglet, lying in the sparse shade of these two structures, was not asleep. He was watching the floor of the desert crack in the heat and he was sniffing for peccary scents.

The blue of the sky changed to colorless white. The sun burned higher. It shone down on the fields

14

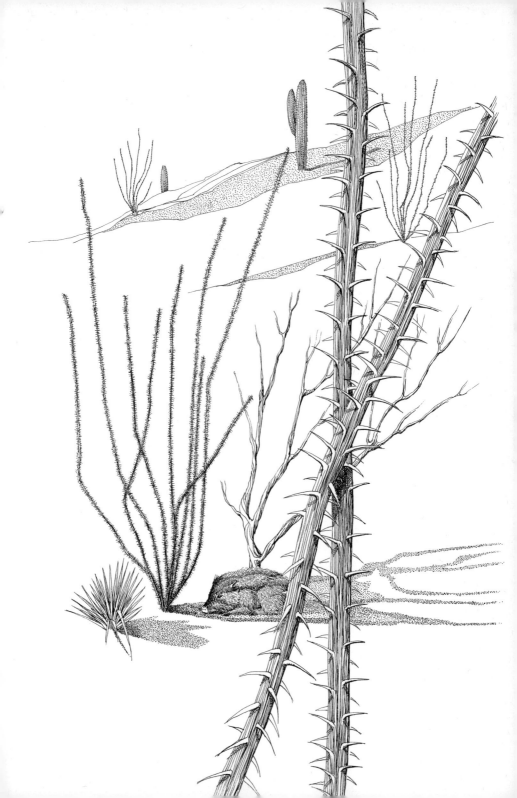

in the mid-central states where the corn was coming into tassel. In the Southeast it fell on cotton cultivators weeding the rows for the last time this year. From Texas to New Jersey the sun warmed the backs of diggers who were harvesting the first potatoes of the year.

All over the country the heat of July brought out insects by the billions. From Texas to Canada grasshoppers tried new wings. Ants, bees, and wasps crept and buzzed in the sun. Butterflies decorated gardens, and at dusk in the Northeast, fireflies flicked cool lights on and off as they spiraled slowly to the tops of the trees. They drifted down to rest at midnight.

Beneath the ocotillo, the piglet listened to the comforting noises of the insects. Then they became quiet. Everything was still in the noon heat. The piglet stood up, slightly concerned that his family had not found him. Stepping to the left, he slipped against a rock. It rolled and plunged into the wash, frightening a cactus wren who had retreated to her nest to escape the heat.

Her nest was an enormous pile of grass stuffed, miraculously, in a jumping cactus. She had no young, for it was July and her offspring were out

16

of the nest now. In the north the moon of July would end the nesting season of the songbirds. Only the goldfinch, the last of the birds to nest, would be building soft cups of thistledown when the August moon arose.

Hurrying along, the piglet walked between tight clumps of plants. They grew in clusters because they did not compete for the sun, as do plants elsewhere in the world, but for the shade. They grew up in each other's shadows so they would not get sunburned. As time passed and still his family did not surround him, the piglet moved with less confidence. He jogged in and out of the plant clumps.

A rustle above his head caught his attention. He could not see that it was a desert woodpecker, for like all peccaries he was nearsighted. The bird alighted on a huge saguaro cactus, fifty feet high and two hundred years old. The plant was shriveled, for it had been months since it had taken up water. The reservoir of water stored inside the cactus was almost gone.

The woodpecker was searching for insects. Suddenly he squawked and flew away. An elf owl had startled him to flight. The tiny owl, no more than three inches high, had two diminutive young in an old woodpecker hole in the saguaro. When he heard the woodpecker he had come to the entrance of the nest, spread his wings over his face like demonic fingers, and peered at the bird. This was the elf owl's way of scaring enemies. It was successful. The woodpecker departed and the owl retreated to the cool hollow and his sleepy young. By the end of the July moon all the elf owls on the desert would have their offspring out of their nests and hunting grasshoppers and crickets. In October they would migrate south and spend the winter months on the southernmost end of the North American Desert.

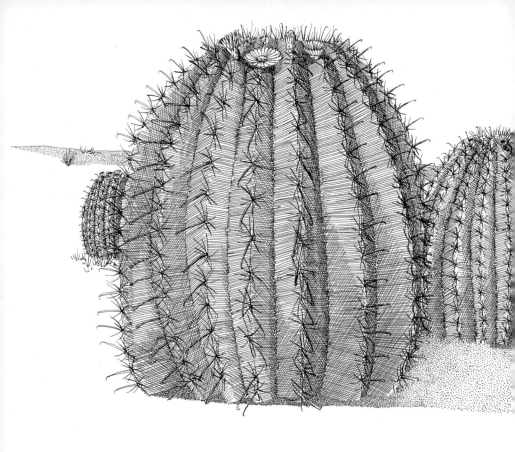

His teeth clattering in anxiety, the piglet came to a rock, hesitated, and turned left. A cluster of desert marigolds bobbed as he created a small wind in passing. Nearby were cacti flowers, blooming before the July rains. Those of the barrel cacti were just unfolding. Most of the bright wild flowers that color the desert had faded in April and their plants had died. Like all life in the desert, these spring flowers have developed a method to protect

themselves against drought. They grow soon after the winter drizzles, bloom for several weeks, then go to seed and die. Their seeds lie in the burning ground waiting for another year.

The sweet-scented mesquite trees had gone to seed. Long brown beans, fruits, hung down from their limbs. Many desert plants fruited in July, among them the saguaro cacti and the jojoba (ho ho' ba) bushes.

Not far from the marigolds, the weary piglet stumbled down a slope of rocks. From his den a male tarantula as large as a man's fist peered near-sightedly into the hot sun. Fuzzy, bearlike, this the largest of the North American spiders lifted his front feet to attack the intruder. But the piglet had slid to the bottom of the incline. Lying on his side in the shade of a cactus, he snorted weakly.

The spider backed into his retreat out of the sun. He was ten years old, just the age to seek a mate. For several nights now he had been roaming the desert trying to court the tempestuous females of his species. This required enormous skill.

First he had to tease a female until she grew

angry and attacked. As she raised her poison fangs to strike him a deadly blow he would snatch them quickly with his feet. Holding them tightly he would slip his special feet, those that carried his sperm, into pockets on her belly. Then he would let go and slip away before the female could bite him.

The male was quite prepared for this adventurous enterprise. Usually he went out by night, but any disturbance during the day started him off to conquer. Sparked into action by the clang of the piglet's hoofs, he had walked into the sunlight. He did not go far. Spider wisdom, evolved through generations of living on the hot desert, turned him back from the sun's blast.

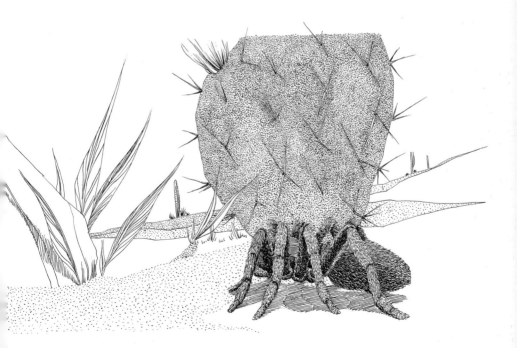

A round-tailed ground squirrel, her family raised and sent off to seek their fortunes, was also under the sunlit floor. She was estivating, sleeping through the heat and drought of summer days and nights.

The cooler soil below the hot desert surface is a daytime retreat for many animals. Riddled with tunnels, runways, and sleeping quarters, the ground is a city of animals. In rooms and corridors rest scorpions, mice, foxes, squirrels, even owls. The dainty kit foxes, tiny foxes of the desert, nap in round earthen hollows, scratched and tramped to smoothness. In July, beneath the burning floor, the female rattlesnakes lie pregnant, waiting for August to give birth to live young. This is an unusual occurrence in the snake world, for most snakes lay eggs.

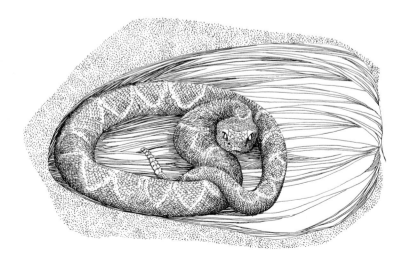

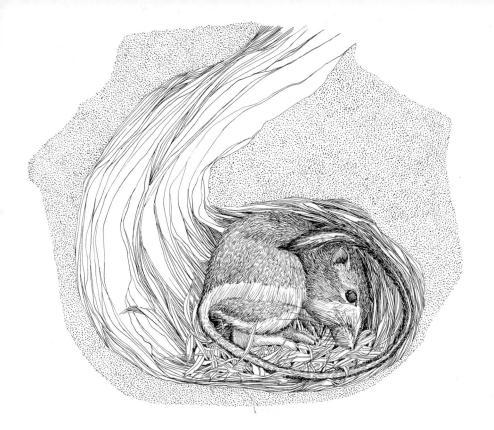

A banner-tailed kangaroo rat curled tighter in another subterranean den. Big-eyed, softly furred, this rodent has large hind legs and a fuzzy black brush at the end of a long graceful tail. Of all the desert animals the lack of water bothers him least. He even eats dry seeds. From them he gets only the tiniest amount of water, but this is enough. His kidneys are so superior they make use of every trace of it. He wastes only occasional drops in urination. He never pants or perspires.

Other desert animals were awake, but avoiding the noon heat in the shade of trees and cacti. One of these was a jackrabbit, who with his long ears and long legs had more body surface than his northern relatives. The more surface an animal has, the more heat leaves its body and the cooler it remains.

Lying in the shade himself, the piglet whined with loneliness for his clan.

Unlike other social animals, the peccaries are casual about their relationships. No one individual seems to lead the clan to food and shelter. The females do not teach their young as carefully as a mother house cat. Instead they simply go about their business, and the little ones like the piglet follow and learn. Good at sensing danger, the sows often take over the sentinel watch while the clan sleeps. When danger approaches—hunters, lions, dogs—the sentinels raise the bristles on their backs and clash their teeth. This sends the clan deeper into their cave. Sometimes it simply sends them clattering in all directions. When they are spread out, they are more difficult for enemies to see and catch.

Affectionate animals, the peccaries like being with each other. Sows often nurse any little piglet that comes along.

The piglet now wanted milk. He wanted to find his clan. He whined and sniffed for his mother. Presently he jumped up. The faint scent of his clan was on the air. He ran. Even the blasting heat could not stop him. His hoofs made dust clouds.

27

The scent led him to the nest of a pack rat. It was a three-foot pile of jumping cacti, the sticky enemy of the piglet. The rat had carried the joints to his spot between two prickly pears by taking each one carefully in his teeth and dragging it gingerly between his front feet.

The piglet circled the rat pile eagerly, but also cautiously. The scent of his clan was somewhere on this spiny castle. He passed a slingshot the rat had carried to his den; there was a bottle top and a road map too. At last he came to the scent. He sat down in discouragement. It lay on but one cholla joint, a joint the rat had found along the trail the peccaries took to the wash. The piglet got up, turned left, and slowly stumbled on.

A crackling rattle catapulted him backward into a prickly pear. His bristles arose along his spine. Scrambling for a footing, he turned, skidded, then ran full tilt around a mesquite tree into the wash. He stood still. Not hearing the rattle any longer, he lay down on his pink belly and stared at the mountainside.

His fear of the rattler had been born two weeks before. The big boar had come upon just such a

deadly tiger rattlesnake in the trail. He had grunted a clarion call. The clan had stopped. Seeing the snake, with the pit in its head that marks all the poisonous snakes of America except the coral snake, they had clattered their teeth. The gray boar pawed the ground. The snake coiled, his tongue darted, and he sensed the heat given off by the mammals.

For several minutes the clan stared, then grew bored and started off. The piglet, still frightened by the clattering teeth, had run between his mother's legs.

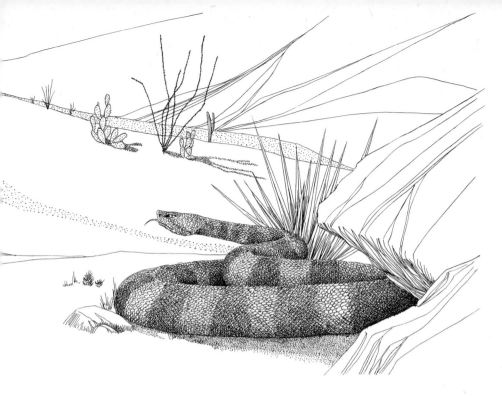

Now there were no legs and he trembled.

When he quieted down he realized he was breathing in the scent of his clan once more. Leaping to his pointed toes he scrambled up the wash. Again he slumped in disappointment. The odor was his own. He had gone left and left and left in a big circle and was right back where he had started from—the greenish stone where he had blundered past the lizard. He whimpered and lay down in the sun. Fear tingled like a spiny fire in his belly.

A tiny dragon of the desert was startled in her

daytime retreat by the piglet's frightened move-
ments. Sporting spikes and spines and scaly ar-
mor, the horned lizard ran a few feet on the hot
clay, then skittered to cover. She would lay eggs
toward the end of the month, then leave them to
hatch thirty days later. Eager to get out of the
sunlight, she did not see the piglet. Had she taken
a better look she might have shot a stream of blood
from her eyes to protect herself. The horned lizard
has one of the most astonishing means of self-
defense of all the animals in the world.

As the dragon hid in the shade, the piglet
rolled his eyes hopelessly toward the sky. The sun
had passed its apex and was starting down. No

wind stirred. The heat was a hundred and twenty degrees and painful. He wailed.

A family of Gambel quail sitting in the bushes heard the weird piglet-cry and ran to another bush. The parents were delicate and bluish-gray. A single plume like a unicorn's horn curled out from their heads. They ran with swiftness. Behind them came five little quail running on feet that moved so fast they could not be seen. The size of twenty-five-cent pieces, the fragile brown-and-yellow chicks peeped and called as they skittered into the shade behind their parents.

The piglet heard no answer to his cry. He lay down beside the greenish stone and waited. Surely his clan would come to nose and pamper and save him from his plight.

As the sun dropped westward a road runner got up and crossed the wash. Her beak was longer than her head and her tail longer than her body. Awkward-looking, this ground-dweller of the cuckoo family was as swift as the automobiles she seemed to race. She came to a stop on a rock and cocked her head sidewise to look at the sky. A buzzard flew beneath a purple cloud that had formed above the Tucson Mountains. Then a lizard stirred. With the speed of a Cadillac the road runner was upon it. She gulped it, but since it was too large to eat all at once she contented herself with digesting the head while the tail hung from her beak.

She hurried back into the brush where her nest lay hidden. Having just raised one brood, she was preparing to lay more eggs in the same nest. She sat down, glanced at the sky, and lifted her feathers to ventilate her body.

The purple cloud dispersed. The sky was clear and white once more. The piglet pressed tighter against the stone.

Presently a veil of vapor appeared where the purple cloud had been. Slowly, it swelled upward and thickened into a thunderhead. Other clouds formed, their tops white and puffy, their bottoms black and flat. Like a bear-growl, the distant roll of thunder sounded. The piglet had never heard this before and he lifted his head.

A bright red cardinal responded to the cloud voice too. He sang a tentative song and was silent. Across the desert the mourning doves bleated.

36

Then they, too, hushed. The clouds piled higher and higher.

Next the piglet heard the wind. The still ocotillo bushes swished. The leafless paloverdes whispered.

It was dark. The piglet shivered. This was not the desert as he knew it, and he grunted in annoyance. Light sizzled all around him. Jagged knives of fire shot out of the clouds. A crack of thunder rocked the earth. The tops of the mountains disappeared. A mouse and a gray fox darted out of the wash where the piglet huddled. A family of quail passed him as they hurried across the dry river bottom and climbed the bank.

The piglet looked out upon a wild world. The clouds fired electric bolts so numerous that the desert floor flickered. Thunder roared endlessly.

Then the rain fell. Great drops as big as the piglet's hoofs bounced on the hot dry soil. They fell faster and faster, until the piglet could no longer see the other side of the wash. The drops became sheets, silvered by the lightning. Thunder drummed, and the piglet heard what all the desert life feared!

High up the wash a trickling whisper began. It grew louder. It roared. The piglet listened. The sound was water, pouring down every rock and cactus into the wash. The wash filled, suddenly and completely. Splashing and rumbling and tearing at everything in its path, the water plunged toward the piglet. He lay still, not knowing what to do.

Suddenly he heard voices new to him. The frogs and toads were singing, their bleating notes rising above the crash of rain. They sang, for this was their hour, their moment to come from their deep dark hideouts below the desert floor. They defied the dryness in their own way. Waiting for July, they came up out of river bottoms when it rained,

quickly mated and quickly laid their eggs. Their
young developed swiftly—in little more than a
week as compared to two months for their New
England relatives. They must grow fast, for their
water would soon be gone.

As the toads and frogs sang out, a bolt of lightning fringed with teeth of fire struck a saguaro
cactus not fifteen feet from the piglet. With this,
the piglet shot up the bank. He ran like a road
runner through the waterfalls of rain. Behind him
the cactus glowed like a firebrand, and every spine
lit up and burned.

But the piglet did not see it. Nor did he see the wall of water tear down the wash, lift his stone, and roll it like a pebble to the valley. He had rounded the Red Rock—and there was his mother, ten feet from where he'd last seen her.

She and his clan stood heads down under an overhang. The piglet ran under her legs. She nosed him and clattered her teeth.

The storm passed. The hot sun shone again. Every rock and hill dripped. Eight-inch-long centipedes came out of cracks and rocks and rippled

along looking for insects to eat. The great saguaro cacti swelled, as each took up thousands of pounds of water with its surface web of waiting roots. Tiny leaves appeared on the leafless paloverdes and the gray ocotillo plants shimmered and turned green. Water trickled, and quail, mice, deer, and peccaries drank thirstily.

Then, as swiftly as it had come, the rain sank into the porous earth and was gone.

That night the moon of July shone down on a renewed desert and a tired tan piglet, snuggled in the middle of his clan.

ABOUT THE AUTHOR

Jean Craighead George has been fascinated by the natural world all her life, and her books are based on her many experiences with the animals she writes about and on the countless books, articles, and scientific papers she reads. THE THIRTEEN MOONS has grown out of her special interest in ecology—particularly in phenology, the study of the relationship between climate and periodic biological events. As part of her research for *The Moon of the Wild Pigs,* Mrs. George visited the Arizona-Sonora Desert Museum, where she talked with scientists and observed the peccaries in their natural habitat.

Mrs. George is co-author of *Dipper of Copper Creek,* which received the Aurianne Award for the most outstanding animal story published in 1957. *My Side of the Mountain, The Summer of the Falcon, Gull Number 737, Spring Comes to the Ocean, Coyote in Manhattan,* and the books in THE THIRTEEN MOONS series have all affirmed her remarkable sensitivity both to nature and to young people.

Mrs. George is a regular contributor of nature stories to *Reader's Digest.* She has held the position of art editor for *Pageant* magazine and has served as a newspaper reporter for the *Washington Post* and International News Service.

ABOUT THE ILLUSTRATOR

Peter Parnall's childhood was spent in several different parts of the United States, including the Mojave Desert; Fort Davis, Texas; and New Haven, Connecticut. As a boy, he kept many pets and started hunting at the age of six. His interest in the outdoors now extends to the training of hawks and owls, and the creation of a new species of game bird.

Mr. Parnall attended Cornell University and Pratt Institute. At various times he worked as an air-hammer operator, a garage mechanic, a hand on a horse farm, and a tire salesman. After settling on a career, he became an advertising art director and a free-lance designer of packages and trademarks. Mr. Parnall has illustrated several children's books. Two of his titles were named, in the same year, to *The New York Times'* list of ten best illustrated books.

Mr. Parnall and his family live in Milford, New Jersey.

S 376-75

599.7
GEO
GEORGE, JEAN
CRAIGHEAD
The moon of the wild
pigs

3.63

DATE DUE			
MAY 28 '91			
SEP 27 '91			
OCT 22 '93			
OCT 6 '94			
NOV 23 '95			
			ALESCO